Children in Suffolk have been delighted by the story of Sammy the Sea Squi[...]
When they hear it as part of our mental health progra[...]
it's always the story that is loved and remembered by p[...]
not just for its quirky characters, but also for its imp[...]

With this book we are sharing the exciting experience of hearing this tale
with more children across Suffolk, and in fact the world.

Our dream of turning this story into a published book, and making it available
to more people, has now become a reality thanks to our fantastic supporters.

We have worked alongside Public Health Suffolk
and our amazing illustrator, Emma Graham,
to ensure that children and adults can read the story of Sammy the Sea Squirt
and bring to life the positive link between movement and mental health.

This book has been printed using vegetable-based inks

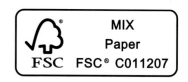

MIX
Paper
FSC FSC® C011207

Paperback: ISBN 978-1-7399138-0-9

First paperback edition September 2021

Story written by Ezra Hewing,
MSc Psychology and Neuroscience of Mental Health, King's College London,
Human Givens Counselling & Psychotherapy PG Dip,
Head of Education at Suffolk Mind

Illustrations and design by Emma Graham
www.egrahamillustrations.co.uk

Printed by FULLERDAVIES
PRINTING & MAILING
www.fullerdavies.co.uk

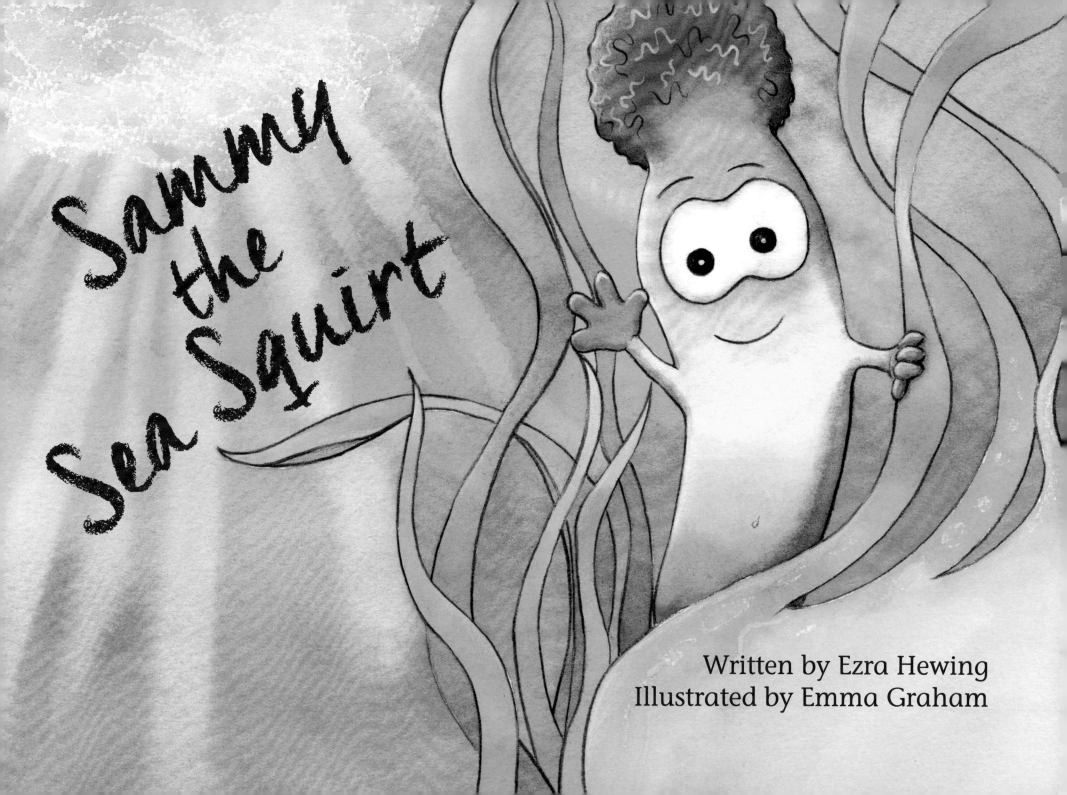

Sammy the Sea Squirt

Written by Ezra Hewing

Illustrated by Emma Graham

Now, under the waves
where sunlight is blue,
Sammy the Sea Squirt
was born with a tube.

Sea squirts have a brain
on top of their tube
that tells them to squirt,
and that's how they move.

SWOOSH!

"I must use my brain
to travel the sea,
and search for a home
for sea squirts like me."

"Who's this I can see?"

"I'm Caleb the Crab!

Crabs move back and forth,
as free as can be,
to scuttle on shore
and under the sea.

My brain, it can choose
to slow down or rush,
but if I don't move
my brain turns to mush!"

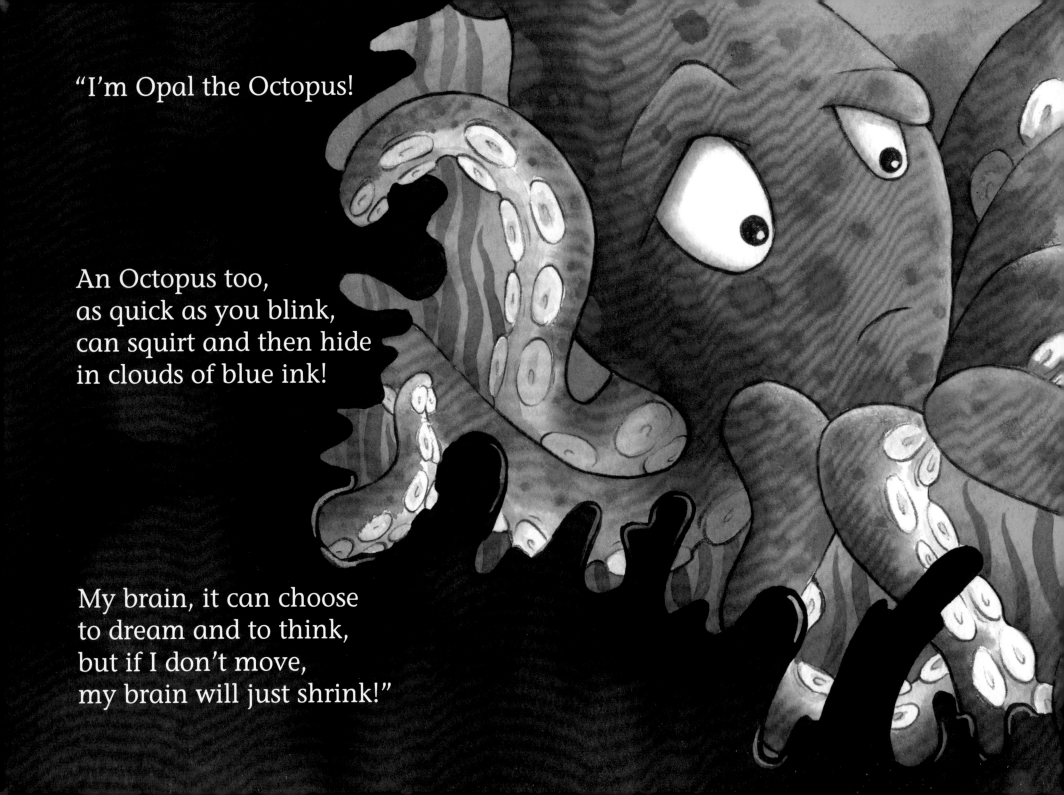

"I'm Opal the Octopus!

An Octopus too,
as quick as you blink,
can squirt and then hide
in clouds of blue ink!

My brain, it can choose
to dream and to think,
but if I don't move,
my brain will just shrink!"

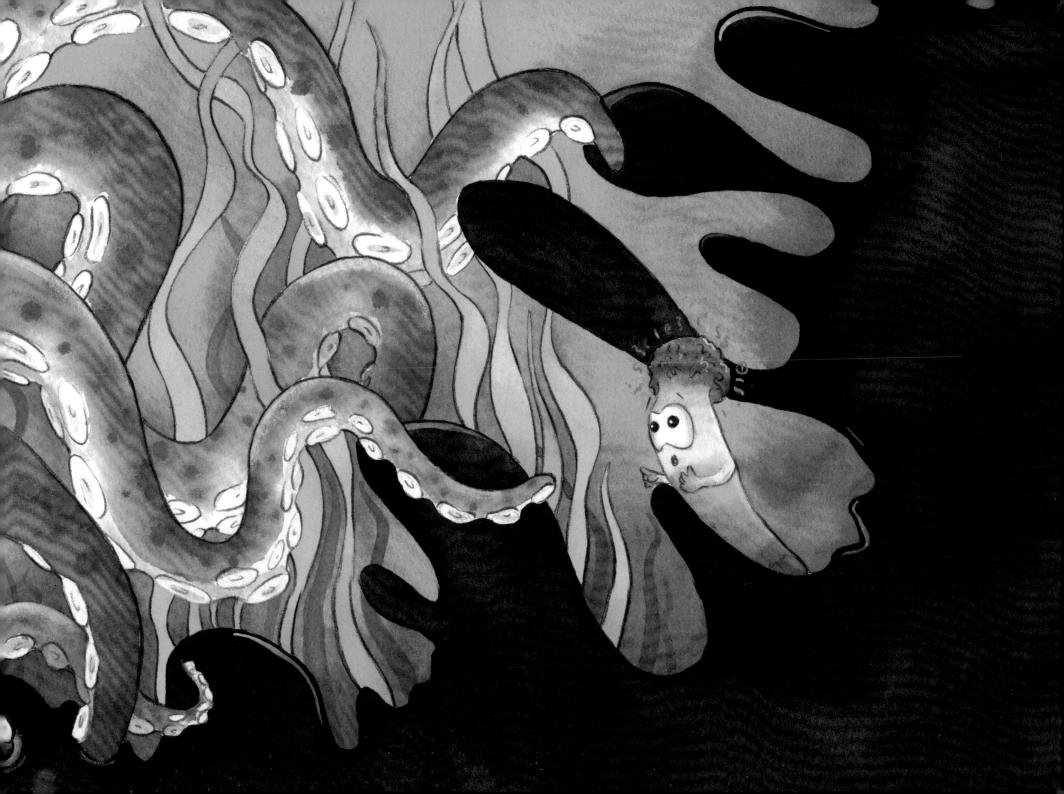

"Then I'll use my brain
to travel the sea,
and search for a home
for sea squirts like me."

"What will I find next?"

SWOOSH!

"I'm Zara the Zebrafish!

My black and white stripes
look just like a zebra.
My brain is a map
and helps me remember...

...the places I've been to,
and those I've not yet.
If I didn't move
I'd surely forget!"

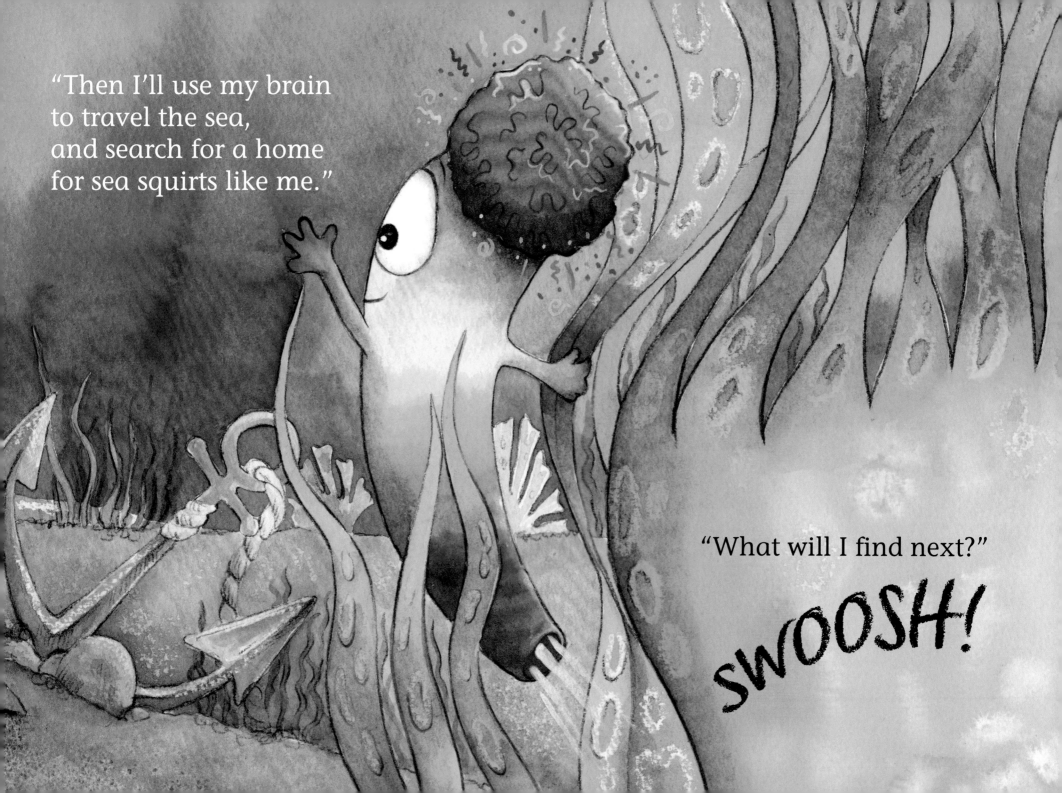

"Then I'll use my brain
to travel the sea,
and search for a home
for sea squirts like me."

"What will I find next?"

SWOOSH!

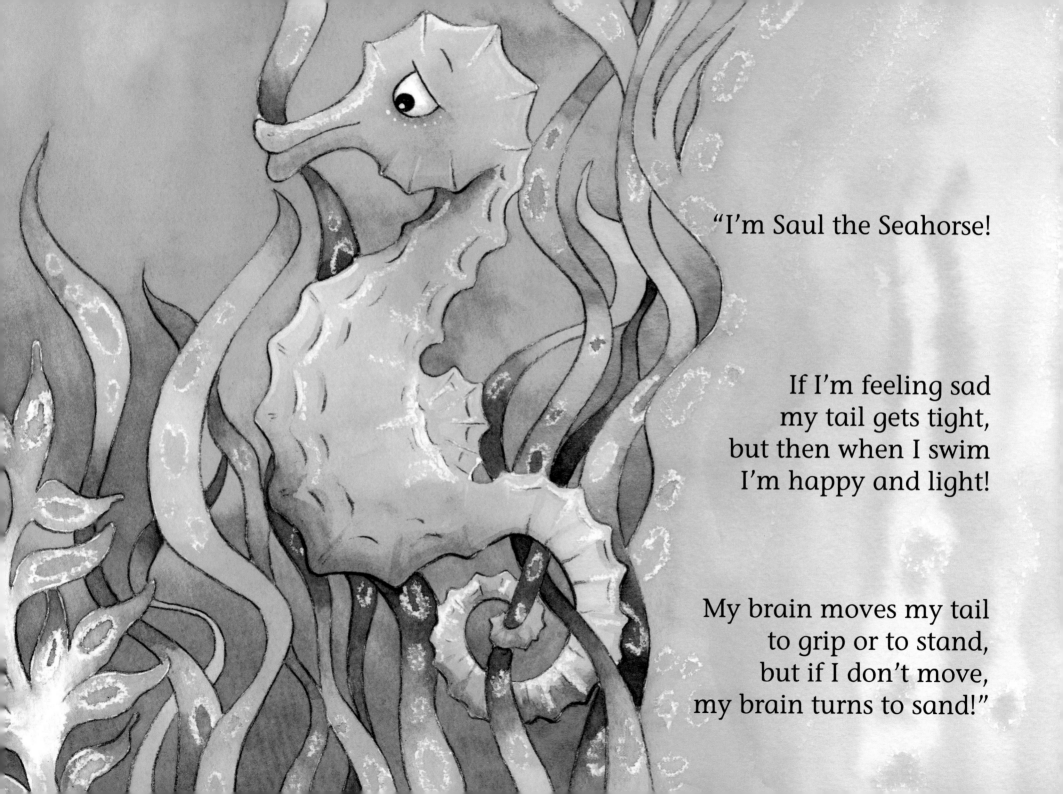

"I'm Saul the Seahorse!

If I'm feeling sad
my tail gets tight,
but then when I swim
I'm happy and light!

My brain moves my tail
to grip or to stand,
but if I don't move,
my brain turns to sand!"

"Then I'll use my brain
to travel the sea,
and search for a home
for sea squirts like me."

"What will I find next?"

SWOOSH!

"They're sea squirts it's true,
but something is strange.
When they find a home
it makes them all change…

The top of their tube
is not quite the same;
when sea squirts don't move
they swallow their brain!"

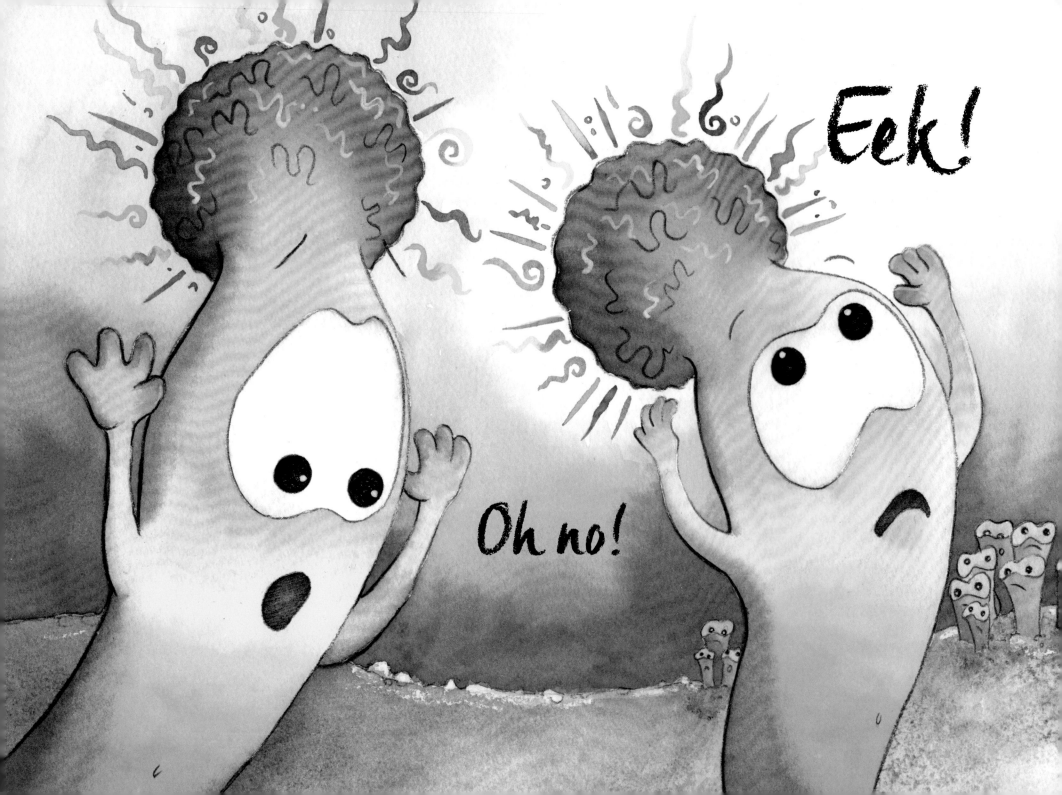

"So I'll use my brain
to travel the sea.

The ocean's the home
for sea squirts like me."

How movement can help children with their mental health

Nobody wants their child to experience poor mental or physical health.

But what can you do to protect them?
How can you support the children in your life to become positive and emotionally resilient adults?

As Sammy the Sea Squirt learns from the creatures they meet on their journey,
movement helps to make the heart and body strong and healthy to protect
and grow healthy brains.

Talking to your child about what Sammy the Sea Squirt learns
about brains and movement can help your child to
remember an important lesson for life.

What is your favourite way to move?

How can you move to keep your brain healthy?
Can you take a deep breath and swoosh like Sammy?

Can you think of a different way to move?

Can you move sideways like Caleb the Crab?

Can you stretch your arms like Opal the Octopus?

Can you flap your fins like Zara the Zebrafish,
or curl your body like Saul the Seahorse?

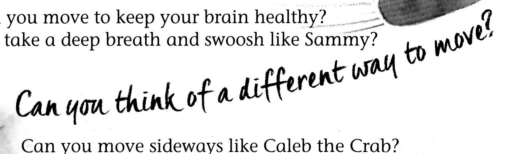

Children chasing each other around the house can drive parents up the wall...

Have you moved today?

But how about having half an hour
when everyone runs around the house
playing hide-and-seek as a family?

If you are out on a walk,
how about challenging them
to run to a landmark,
perhaps a tree in a park, or a post-box?

As well as helping to keep everyone healthy,
movement can burn off energy and calm children down,
so that they can go off to sleep more easily at bedtime.

As you notice your child moving more,
comment on how much stronger,
happier or flexible they seem.
Ask them to notice how they feel too.

Movement releases the brain's endorphins,
which come with feeling good.
When they notice how they feel,
children are more likely to remember
that being physically active is rewarding.
Then they are more likely to want to do it more often –
until it becomes a healthy lifelong habit.

Acknowledgements

Suffolk Mind would like to thank everyone who helped us to make the story of Sammy the Sea Squirt into a book for children and families to enjoy:
With extra special thanks to our patrons Dennis and Charlotte Stevenson

We would also like to thank our donors and sponsors:
Mind, Jo Banthorpe, David Patrick, Jan Patrick, Selene Holden, Associated British Ports, Suffolk Chamber of Commerce, St Luke's Lodge No.225 Ipswich, Gotelee Solicitors LLP, Distag QCS (UK) Ltd & Inderwick, The Willows Primary School, Martlesham Primary Academy, Lakenheath C.P. School, St Joseph's College Ipswich, Gorseland Primary School, Ipswich School, Sebert Wood C.P. School.

As well as those who sponsored the project through our Crowdfunder:
Hardie Thorkild Ambler, Jane Bailey, Beverley de Boos, Jacqueline Bridgeman, Norma Bushell, Catalina Carvajal, Ellen Clayton, V. Constantini, Ruth Crossley, Miles Daffin, Christina Davies, Eva & Otto Dolby, Rachel Downes, Rosalind Erskine, Nan Eshelby, Parris Robinson-Foster, Jo Flack, Mr. Henry Griffin, Fiona Hanlon, William & Rosa Harris, Samantha Holland, Beatrice & Freya Holden, Phil Hopkins, Steve Hume, Shirley Imlach, Julia Johnston, Emma Lightfoot, Jillian Lofts, Rosemary Moss, Rosaleen Palmer, Anne Parkinson, Patricia Parkinson, Mark Power, M & R Quantrill, Kelly Sayers, Ciara Scallon, Del Sharman, Angela Skinner, J Spurgeon, Jamie Stringer, Nigel & Jill Suckling, Ian Thompson, Alan & Joanne Upson, Stephen Watt, Miss Louisa Wells, Andrew Wilesmith, Willow & Daisy.
In addition, thank you to all of our anonymous sponsors and donors.
Your support has enabled us to bring this book to children across Suffolk.

The Sammy the Sea Squirt Project Team
Adam Baker, Kristina Brinkley, Emma Graham, Lizzy Graham, Ginny Idehen, Louise Harris, Ezra, Shahrazad and Noorjahan Hewing, Colin Hopkins, Jon Neal, Lizzy Tuthill & Ellie Winch